The Story of
Saint David

Siân Lewis

Illustrated by
ROGER JONES

Pont

Sixth impression published in 2007 by Pont Books, an imprint of
Gomer Press, Llandysul, Ceredigion, SA44 4JL

First impression – 1995
Second impression – 1997
Third impression – 1998
Fourth impression – 2000
Fifth impression – 2002

ISBN 978 1 85902 230 6
A CIP record for this title is available from the British Library.

The publishers wish to acknowledge the help given by the Welsh Arts Council.

Printed and bound in Wales at
Gomer Press, Llandysul, Ceredigion

When David was a boy he loved to spend time with the holy
men who lived at the monastery. The monks journeyed far,
telling stories from the Bible to the people of Wales.
'Can I come with you?' David asked his friends.
'No, boy,' replied the monks, 'you're much too young.'
'But I can't wait to tell the people about Jesus,' David said.

David was special in many ways. After all, he was a king's son.
Sant, his father, was King of all Ceredigion. Non, his mother,
loved him dearly and was proud of how David had learnt to
read and write. The monks at Henfynyw monastery had
taught him well and the other boys were full of admiration.

'We know that you are special, David,' they told him.
'A white dove always follows you and hovers nearby.'

One of David's teachers was an old man called Paulinus.
He had been blind for many years and could not read for
himself the precious books he loved so much.
One day David placed his hands on the old man's eyes and
suddenly Paulinus could see again. It was a miracle.

'You have a special gift for helping people, David,' said Paulinus. 'It is time for you to leave the monastery. Go and help others and do God's work.'

David was delighted to be on his way, preaching to people wherever he went.

He travelled miles through sunshine, wind and rain, with a stout stick in his hand. He loved to stop and talk to those he met.

'Who is Jesus Christ?' he was often asked.

'Jesus Christ is the Son of God,' answered David.

Everywhere, people wanted to worship God, and David had churches built for them to meet and pray together.

David chose Glyn Rhosyn, a beautiful sheltered valley, as the place for his new monastery. But Boia, the fierce prince who ruled there, had other plans.

'God has told me that I should build here,' said David.
'Ha!' shouted Boia. 'My soldiers will soon get rid of you!'
Yet when the soldiers came, they could not harm him.

So David built his monastery at Glyn Rhosyn and lived there with other holy men. Together they worked the land and kept animals. They helped the poor and those who were sick. David ate simple meals – of bread, water and vegetables.

And always, he prayed and preached
to others.
It was everything David had always
wanted.

One day David travelled to Brefi where hundreds had
come to preach and listen. But the crowds were noisy
and impatient, and no one could see or hear.
'You must preach, David,' urged his friends.
When David began to speak, his voice rang
out clear as a trumpet and the ground
beneath him rose up.
Then everyone could see Saint David
and hear his words.

Saint David died on the first day of March.
'Be happy,' he told his friends, 'and always believe in God.'
Today, St David's cathedral stands where David built his
monastery.
And the people of Wales celebrate, on March 1st, the life of a
very special saint – Saint David.